CROSSING THE LINE:

POWER ACTIVITIES

FOR THERAPY AND LEARNING

MANUAL OF
EQUINE ASSISTED
ACTIVITIES FOR
BOTH LEARNING
AND THERAPEUTIC
PROFESSIONAL

BY:
**BUNNY SUMNER
YOUNG, MA, QMHP**

ILLUSTRATED BY:
ASHLEIGH STROUBE

Young, Bunny Sumner
Crossing the Line: Power Activities for Therapy and Learning

Copyright 2019 by Bunny S. Young
Published by KWE Publishing LLC

ISBN (paperback) – 9780999725481

Contact Bunny Young at:
A Better Place Consulting
https://abetterplaceconsulting.com/
bunny@bunnyyoung.com
804-728-0319

KWE Publishing LLC
Prince George, VA
www.kwepub.com

FOREWORD

Frustration, sadness, anger, depression, anxiety, fear, poor choices and negative behaviors as well as desires to improve school, work, and personal performance, to communicate clearly with compassion, and to live purposefully and intentionally motivates people to seek solutions for themselves, their loved ones, or their workplace. We are learning, or perhaps rediscovering, the power of the horse in teaching lessons essential to living meaningful and productive lives.

We are partnering with horses to heal the mind, heart, and spirit through equine assisted learning (EAL) and equine assisted/facilitated psychotherapy (EAP/EFP). Horses have the ability to help us access knowledge, thoughts and feelings, and practice constructive behaviors in unique and powerful ways.

How do we maximize the impact of our partnerships with horses to effect positive changes within individuals, families, businesses, communities and our world? This manual is an amazing resource to help you to do just that. Translating our intentions, within the scope of our individual roles as educators, psychotherapists, and equine professionals, knowledge, skills, and abilities as practitioners of EAL and EAP/EFP requires both a masterful knowledge of equine behavior and psychology as well as inspired creativity.

What we see and what our students and participants experience often appears to be magic. Yet, while it may appear to be the product of magic, the results we see are research-based activities conducted by professionals who are educated and safely and appropriately implement the best practices of equine assisted activities and therapies (EAAT) in partnership with horses who are emotionally healthy and enjoying a good quality of life.

The positive outcomes of our partnership with other appropriate professionals and our horses are enhanced by the activities that we choose for our students and participants; these are the tools of our profession. While our personal theory of change is our toolbox, the activities are the tools. Developing tools that meet the carefully assessed needs of our students and participants is not every practitioner's strength.

Therefore, this manual provides not only a comprehensive set of activities that can be adapted to safely meet a variety of individual and programmatic needs, but also insightful guidance on ways to adapt them and to interpret the outcomes that you will see.

I have had the pleasure of working alongside Bunny Young for many years in providing EAAT at Dream Catchers at the Cori Sikich Therapeutic Riding Center in Williamsburg, Virginia. I have both mentored her and learned from her. She inspires me and amazes me with her ability to create elegantly simple, safe, and highly effective activities to meet the needs of our students and participants.

The inspired activities in this manual have demonstrated that they are powerful tools for change, and should be used by equine professionals who have a solid knowledge of equine behavior, psychology, and safety in partnership with our magnificent teachers, our horses.

NANCY A. PASCHALL
Executive Director,
*Dream Catchers at the
Cori Sikich Therapeutic Riding Center*

INTRODUCTION

To describe what happens between participant and horse seems impossible at times. There is an unspoken magic exchanged when a horse, a prey animal, opens to the possibility of a deep and authentic relationship with a human, a predator by nature. The use of a horse during a therapy session brings a whole new element to the therapeutic process.

Through focused, customized activities, therapists and educators can make quick progress. Participants physically experience their emotions through a large animal which mirrors their feelings, insecurities, and relationships.

I remember the first time my aunt brought me to the ranch: the smell of leather and hay, the sound of the horse's breath echoing off the cinder block barn walls. I knew then that this was something special and mystical: a relationship of trust, power, communication, and equality.

My first lesson was with my grandparent's quarter horse named Willy. Forget walking and trotting! I immediately wanted to canter with Willy. I fell off a lot that day and learned my first lesson about taking small steps in life and not rushing into things. So many lessons have occurred since that first ride and I can hardly share the depth of what each moment with a horse has taught me.

This manual comes from my experience as a simple cowgirl who took her love of equines and respect for what they teach us and turned it into a career of therapy, retreats, and lessons for professionals. I have been asked by many how I come up with my activities and structure for the lessons and this answer remains the same:

"I never know what the ultimate outcome is for an activity. I simply show up, set up, and share with the horses what the group or individual wants from the day and what they are dealing with in life. The rest of the magic is all the equines."

I hope you enjoy what this manual is about to share with you. I hope you appreciate the stories from each activity, testimonials from past participants, and the incredible illustrations that someone far more talented than me put together to attempt to show you what these activities might look like.

It was my pleasure to put this together for you and share these activities to bring more magic into our world through your programs. Thank you for what you do, what you bring to them, and what your horses dedicate to those you work with.

Happy Trails,

Bunny Young

OVERVIEW & PURPOSE

Equine Assisted Learning (EAL) is used for non-therapeutic populations for learning, teaching, and goal setting. EAL can be used in a variety of ways for individuals and groups or teams. Much like EAL, Equine Assisted Therapy (EAT) is a treatment with clear treatment goals facilitated by a professional utilizing equines in the activities to achieve those goals.

For the sake of this manual we are focusing on Equine Assisted Learning. However, you will notice many of the anecdotes regarding the activities come from therapeutic situations facilitated with a mental health professional present.

So, what is "Crossing the Line"? If you do not have a therapist or professional to develop, evaluate, and support treatment goals present during the session then it is NOT EAT. EAL activities should be approached and designed strictly as learning activities.

It is my opinion that all interaction with a horse or equine is therapeutic. That is both good news and a word of caution. Even if you are doing EAL, be aware of certain symptoms and signs that your participant needs professional support. Always follow proper steps to ensure the safety of everyone involved as well as the horses.

Aside from the supporting players during a session, the processing has most differentiation between EAL and EAT. The questions asked after the activity can be either learning-focused or treatment plan-focused.

For EAL sessions, my advice is to keep your questions about the horse during your feedback.

- What did you notice about the horse during the activity?
- How do you think he/she liked the grooming?
- What was his/her response when strangers entered the pen?
- Why did he/she follow your direction?

There will be emotional and therapeutic parts to these answers. That is unavoidable. However, directing the focus of the processing to the horse provides a verbal buffer. This deflects from the feelings that the person was experiencing during that activity.

When you direct the questions to the human participant, it becomes much deeper and therapeutic.

- How did it make you feel when the horse followed you?
- What did you do during the grooming process to put him/her at ease?

- How did you feel when you entered the pasture with the horses?
- What experiences in your own life parallel what you experienced in this activity?

These questions require that the participant consider their own feelings and emotions to articulate an answer.

EAL
EQUINE ASSISTED LEARNING
Learning, teaching, and goal setting for non-therapeutic populations including individuals and groups or teams.

EAT
EQUINE ASSISTED THERAPY
Goal-oriented activities facilitated by a professional utilizing equines for therapeutic populations.

In summation, there is no true line. It is all therapeutic if you are going to engage in Equine Assisted Activities. If you choose to focus on learning, you can protect the line as much as possible by focusing the processing of the activity on the horse's feelings, reactions, engagement, and interactions. That is the safest way to protect a person's boundaries of therapy versus learning.

NOTE: Whether you are choosing to use EAT or EAL, your equines do not differentiate. They need just as much energy work and release for either activity. Even if a person does not discuss their mental health during a session, it can still stick with the animal. Please ensure that each session has time for the professional to return to the horse and check in to maintain health and well-being of all animals.

EDUCATION STANDARDS

1. For professional use
2. Activities designed to be supported by an equine specialist
3. Horse selection should be heavily considered when practicing activities

OBJECTIVES

1. Partner with equines to provide outcomes that provoke therapeutic feedback in a safe and experiential environment
2. Partner with equines to provide outcomes that provoke educational feedback in a safe and experiential environment

MATERIALS NEEDED

1. Equine Specialist
2. Educator or therapist
3. Proper horse selection according to the Horse Interaction Index

HORSE INTERACTION INDEX

	INTROVERT	EXTROVERT
PASSIVE		
ACTIVE		

DETERMINING WHERE YOUR HORSE FALLS ON THIS INDEX

Does your horse stand lazily at the back of their stall or are they paying attention to everything that is around them and moving closer to activity?

- An active horse will be paying attention to his/her surroundings, ears pricked and eyes bright and will tend to move more overall.
- A passive horse will be much less openly observant about his/her environment and will act much quieter overall.

Do they interact with anyone that comes near their stall or do they simply notice and turn away?

- Extroverted horses will interact with humans, nosing their hands and coming up to greet them.
- Introverted horses will certainly notice the absence or presence of humans, but will not actively interact with them.

PROCESSING
Steps for ensuring proper feedback and processing:

1. Ask open-ended questions
2. Know how to keep away from therapeutic questions if it is a learning group or session
3. Identify when professional intervention or support is needed
4. Create a safe space to care for equines after all sessions

This is a wonderful introductory activity. It is low engagement, low risk, and low pressure. If an individual is afraid of horses or there is a newer group to your program, then herd observation is an ideal starting point. This activity can provide a great sense of the culture and personality of the group or individual in an extremely safe manner. This can form a foundation of relationship to move deeper into through other activities.

Many, like this young girl, have benefited from this activity:

"She told the group that she did not want to come. She feared horses because they were so much bigger than her. She made it clear that she did not want to be here today. The therapist asked if she would just stand outside and watch them for a little bit. She could leave if she still felt the same way but just to watch the horses for a few minutes from afar. She watched the horses for a few minutes. The therapist asked her what she noticed. The young girl began to sob. She explained that the one horse was so lonely and none of the other horses would be friends with it, so that was why the horse just stood at the fence and stared into nothing. The young girl told the therapist that sometimes the horse thought about killing itself. The therapist later shared that up until that moment, the young girl had never confessed or discussed her suicidal thoughts. Her treatment team had no reason to suspect her life was in danger."

OBJECTIVE

Observe how a herd of horses interact naturally in a pasture.

MATERIALS NEEDED: A pasture.
HORSES NEEDED: 2-4 horses (ideally of varying personalities).
SET UP: Allow the horses to be free-roaming in a pasture.

INTRODUCTION

Bring participant(s) outside where they may stand outside of the pasture and watch the horses. Ask participants to make observations about the horses.

- What do they notice about their postures, interactions with other horses, and movement?
- What are their other observations of the horses?

Do not tell the participants the horses' names or genders.

SIDELINES

Encourage participant(s) to notice the horse's response to the group or individual approaching.

- Did any of the horses react to an unexpected sound made on the ranch?
- How did one horse react to the other horses?

If the equine professional and therapist decide it is appropriate, add another horse to the pasture to give the group an opportunity to observe how the herd reacts to a new member of the group.

PROCESSING POINTS/APPLICATION

Horses mirror feelings and emotional states of humans[1].

- How did the participant(s)' observations reflect their own inner state?
- After the participant(s) have had an opportunity to spend some time observing the horses, tell them the horses' names, and note if they are male or female.

THERAPEUTIC OUTCOME

The expected therapeutic outcome for this activity is for participants to practice mindful observation of the horses. The hope is that participants will be able to notice the subtle interactions the horses had with each other and their reactions to a group of strangers approaching the pasture.

This observation activity can provide participants an opportunity to apply some of their insight into their own recovery. They can compare the herd interaction with their own interactions with family members or loved ones. Seeing how such a powerful animal can be peaceful and quiet can also be a powerful tool to relieve anxiety.

Self-care is the foundation of health, both physical and mental. Your ability to care for yourself and put your needs first allows for everything else in your journey to have appropriate energy, support, and fulfillment. Without attention to self-care, there can be no sustainable plan to improve mental health, achieve personal or professional life goals, or have healthy relationships. Through the habit of grooming, horses teach us how the act of caring and grooming can lead to a safer, more sustainable, and all around better ride.

"**W**hen he saw his horse, he wanted to just jump on its back. He did not want to listen to the equine specialist about the importance of grooming. Reluctantly he helped as they brushed his horse and began to pick his hooves. When they got to his rear right hoof the boy noticed a large stone in the frog of the hoof. He realized if he had not taken the steps to groom and prepare his horse and rushed into the ride he would have seriously hurt his horse who was his best friend. He promised that he would always start with grooming before every ride so he could ensure that both he and his best friend were safe and happy."

OBJECTIVE

To build a relationship with a chosen horse through caring for it in the stall. This can include grooming the horse, talking to the horse, petting the horse, sharing a secret with the horse, or any other ways the participant wants to bond with the horse.

MATERIALS NEEDED: This is an individual activity done in the comfort of the horse's stall. A grooming box can be made accessible if the participant chooses to use these tools. An equine specialist will need to observe but not interfere.

HORSES NEEDED: Passive introverted or passive extroverted horses, depending on whether the participant is introverted or extroverted. Do not use a horse that does not enjoy a stall or being groomed. (Refer to the Horse Interaction Index.)

SET UP: Depending on the barn size and group size, have two more horses than participants to allow for choice and to ensure everyone gets a horse. Set grooming boxes outside of the stalls for time efficiency. Only use horses that do not mind being in their stalls or being groomed in their stalls. Some horses do not like this activity, and that should be respected.

INTRODUCTION

Explain to the participants that the objective of the activity is to get to know the chosen horse. Allow them to walk down the barn aisle and choose a horse. Once they have chosen a horse, have the equine specialist open the stall door for the participant and allow them to enter and set the grooming box in the front corner of the stall right against the door. Have the equine specialist explain that this is so the horse does not step on the box. Share the horse's name with the participant. Given only that information, it is now the participant's task to get to know the horse.

SIDELINES

Ensure that the equine specialist maintains visual view of participants while they are in the stalls to be able to provide cues if unsafe behaviors are observed. The therapist could say to the group, towards the end of the activity, something like, "Now that you have formed a relationship, it might be safe to share something with your new partner that you have not told anyone else."

PROCESSING POINTS/ APPLICATION

Good questions to ask during this processing might be:

- "What was your horse's story?"
- "How do you think your horse felt?"
- "How did you feel caring for another being?"
- "Did your horse trust you?"
- "How did it feel telling your horse a secret?"

Allow for group feedback from others regarding the responses to these questions. This is a good activity with which to end the day because it allows the participants to remain in a calm place and come down to a neutral state of mind before returning home or to an inpatient treatment facility.

THERAPEUTIC OUTCOME

The expected therapeutic outcome for each participant is to create a safe space to bond with a horse. Most of the time, this will allow for a bond or trust to begin to form, although that is not the goal of the activity. It is simply to allow the participant to feel safe while in the presence of a horse. Allowing the independence of just participant and horse in a stall can be intimidating, but it can also feel liberating.

Participants are given the opportunity to share secrets with another being that they can be positive will not share with any human. This can begin a relief process for participants who have suffered trauma or depression[2]. The tactile stimulation of petting or grooming an animal releases endorphins and increases levels of serotonin in the brain associated with happiness and decreased depression[3]. This activity ties into the bond and partnership.

ACTIVITY #3: ISSHOES
(ISSUES+HORSESHOES=ISSHOES)

Sometimes equine experiential learning does not even require an actual horse to be present. We can use this activity to identify obstacles, themes, or issues for an individual or a group. We are not always aware of the physical burden our "stuff" and stress we carry around each day can have on us. By carrying this representation of your burdens, your attention is drawn to what is preventing you from living your life.

You can feel the weight and notice the inconvenience. We draw attention to this token of what we invisibly burden ourselves with to encourage us to drop our issues sooner rather than later. This is a great activity for teams and groups.
*You can have participants carry more than one horseshoe! *

Caution: DO NOT use this activity with participants with violent tendencies.

"As the group worked to saddle the horse, the horseshoe that Joe was carrying almost hit the horse on the side. Joe had picked a rusty, sharp horseshoe to represent his relationship with his coworker. Another member cautioned him to be more careful as to not hurt the horse. Joe then became frustrated and explained he could not complete the activity with the horseshoe in his hand as he did not want to hurt the horse and it was hard to do anything with just one hand. He then looked up and then back at his hand. He stated, 'I can either figure out how to improve this relationship with my coworker so that it does not hurt anyone else, or I need to find a way to let it go and move on so that I can accomplish the things that I want to and not let this issue get in my way of success'. He shared that having a physical indication of how this rusty dangerous relationship was impacting him completing his goals was exactly what he needed to make the decision to move on."

OBJECTIVE

To create a physical association for participants to experience and relate the horseshoe as a metaphor for emotional or mental burdens that the participants carry in their lives. To identify coping skills and tools to ease these burdens.

MATERIALS NEEDED: A bucket of horseshoes, preferably varying styles, weights, sizes, ages, and conditions. (Be mindful that remaining nails can be meaningful but dangerous).
HORSES NEEDED: None.
SET UP: Place bucket in safe area where participants can congregate.

INTRODUCTION

Ask participants to pick up one horseshoe from the bucket, and when they pick each one up to identify aloud what burden related to living with trauma or depression that horseshoe represents. Participants are asked to hold onto each horseshoe that they choose. When all participants have their horseshoes, explain that participants must carry these horseshoes around for the remainder of the session.

They must not place their horseshoe(s) in their pockets, set them down, ask someone else to carry them, or leave them behind. Each horseshoe will represent the burden that the participants identified when they picked the horseshoe up. Ask the participants to think about how this burden relates to their rehabilitation work with trauma and depression in their lives.

SIDELINES

If a participant asks another member of the group for help holding their horseshoe, this is meaningful. If someone leaves his or her "issues" behind or drops it, this is a good processing tool to determine how participants deal with their issues in their lives. It is acceptable to have horseshoes with nails and rust; people's issues are not pretty or comfortable.

Prolonged exposure to the feelings of trauma or depression in a controlled and safe environment with professionals there to support the participant can lead to a healthy emotional processing[4]. Contrary

to a traditional office setting where the participant would simply hold the horseshoes for the duration of the session, with this activity the participant is walking around the facility, engaging in activities, and possibly working with other group members, all while managing his or her physical burden of a horseshoe that represents the burdens associated with the rehabilitation journey.

PROCESSING POINTS/ APPLICATION

- How do people handle their issues?
- How do they carry their issues around (physically and emotionally)?
- Who can help them with their issues?
- How do those issues affect others around them?
- How do they affect their ability to complete what is needed of them?
- How safe are they?
- How does it feel to let the issues go?
- What impact do the issues have on a person after carrying them for a while?
- How do they hurt a person and others around that person?
- Are these burdens necessary?
- How much control does a person have over them?

By asking some or all of these questions, the professionals can challenge the participant's negative thought patterns that he or she is suffering from related to trauma and depression. By challenging these thought patterns and beginning to practice new ones, participants can begin to have more confidence and self-esteem rather than being depressed or traumatized[5].

THERAPEUTIC OUTCOME

The expected therapeutic outcome for this activity is for participants to associate the physical burden of carrying a horseshoe with the emotional and mental burden of coping with a traumatic opportunity to make a real-life application of a healthy experience and depression. Each

participant will have the opportunity to make a real-life application of a healthy coping skill for the emotions generated from this activity.

By the end of the activity, participants should be able to take their horseshoe and let it go, leaving (or beginning to leave) the horseshoe and the burden it represented behind at this session. This physical release can be very meaningful for a participant. The somatic release can trigger new positive thought patterns in the brain. The mindfulness of positive thinking by releasing the issue can lead to increased positive thinking in other areas of the participant's rehabilitation[6].

We all have crap in our lives: some of it is useful, some of it is not. Some may not be our crap, but we still must deal with it. Through this exercise, we can openly discuss what the crap is in our lives, apply symbolic and metaphoric meanings for what we are dealing with, and have open discussions about how we deal with it.

CAUTION: Blindfolding someone who has been traumatized can trigger a traumatic episode or flashback for the participant. Therapists should be mindful of their participants and ask permission prior to blindfolding.

"She had the shovel in her hand when she felt her boot sink into what no longer felt like grass. Rather than telling the group, which was blindfolded just like she was, that she had found the pile of crap that they were searching for, she pulled her boot out, took a step to the left and kept walking. The group wandered around for another 20 minutes in frustration. When we processed, the therapist called her attention to her choice when she encountered the pile. The female participant responded 'Well that is about right. I do whatever I can to avoid dealing with the crap in my life and avoid it at all costs.'"

OBJECTIVE

To provide the group or individual an opportunity to explore coping skills when not all senses are available and when faced with obstacles in their lives.

MATERIALS NEEDED: For every six participants: 1 mucking bucket, 1 broom, 1 rake, and 3 mucking forks.
HORSES NEEDED: Either no horses, or if appropriate, 1-2 introverted/passive horses (Substitute horse type if different behavior is more appropriate for group). (Refer to the Horse Interaction Index.)
SET UP: Place mucking tools in bucket along fence line near entrance to pasture that group or individual will be mucking. Put horses out at liberty if chosen (not tied to any post or fence but free to range) in the pasture in which the group or individual will be working.

INTRODUCTION

Start participants in a safe area and provide them with blindfolds. Have participants blindfold themselves. Instruct them to find the pasture (Use either a number or descriptor to assist them in differentiating the pastures) and muck that pasture.

If needed, the professional can allow the group to ask three questions. This information is not shared with the group until after they have been blindfolded. This practice minimizes non-verbal cues from other group members. Do not explain what mucking means to the group unless they specifically use a question for that purpose.

Assure all participants that the professionals will keep them safe. (This should be stated first when expectations for the day are set at the beginning of the session so that the therapist is repeating it prior to beginning this exercise).

Note: Mucking is the act of shoveling horse manure into a bucket or out of a horse's leisure area using a wide mucking fork. This usually occurs in a pasture or stall.

SIDELINES

If the mental health professional or equine specialist suspects that someone is cheating or peeking through their blindfold, they can choose to hold the participant accountable for their actions by sharing the suspicions with the group or removing them from the group, removing their blindfold, and silencing their ability to speak. This allows the participant to experience problem solving feelings of being able to see but not assist their other group members who are still blindfolded.

Then participants can apply this experience to family members or friends who have witnessed their struggle with trauma or depression but felt powerless to help them. They may see how they could allow those family members or friends to help in their rehabilitation[6].

The loss of a sense can be applied to substance abuse that is common among those who suffer from trauma or depression. Example questions:

- What senses are lost or minimized when you drink?
- How capable are you then at recognizing your surroundings or keeping yourself safe?[7]

PROCESSING POINTS/ APPLICATION

Some of the possible processing points include: losing one of one's senses, working as a group, dealing with a difficult task, facing obstacles that are not pleasant, knowing the result before knowing the steps to get there, choosing proper tools, assumptions, leadership, frustration, healthy coping skills, loss of control, and substance abuse. Group activities, such as the ones listed above, can facilitate group interaction in a way that traditional clinical therapy may lack[8]. The difficulty of coping with a loss in general can present an opportunity for processing in a safe, controlled environment, which can expedite the healing and rehabilitative process for participants suffering from trauma or depression[4].

The additional stimulation of being outdoors in an unfamiliar place like a barn or pasture can add stressors for participants that encourage them to use their coping skills. In a traditional clinical therapy setting (inside an office on a comfortable couch), it would be difficult to create an experience like this activity where the participant could be stimulated by so many things and create a level of controlled uncomfortability to work on healthy coping.

By using equine-assisted psychotherapy for rehabilitation with participants who suffer from trauma or depression, a mental health professional is dedicated to the therapeutic relationship with the participant and supporting that relationship. If the mental health professional were to try to recreate an uncomfortable situation for a participant in an office, it could compromise that relationship[9]. In equine-assisted psychotherapy, the level of stressors is immediately present for the participant merely by being around large animals and in an unfamiliar or new setting while blindfolded.

THERAPEUTIC OUTCOME

The expected therapeutic outcome for this activity is that each participant will learn at least two healthy coping skills when presented with a challenging situation. The participants will learn to build trust for one another and their own senses as they navigate unfamiliar ground and situations.

Participants will, hopefully, be able to verbalize an emotion that they experienced during this activity and why they feel they experienced that emotion. (Example: frustration due to the loss of control in not being able to see.) Coping with the loss of one of a participant's senses can be applied to his or her rehabilitation process by processing which senses are lost when he or she experiences a flashback from PTSD or are too depressed to taste food.

Professionals can ask the participants how they cope with limited use of their senses during these periods of time and what that experience feels like. This discussion will help participants to make real life applications for the emotions generated because of this activity and to a traumatic situation or a time they have felt depressed in their lives and felt out of control of their senses[6].

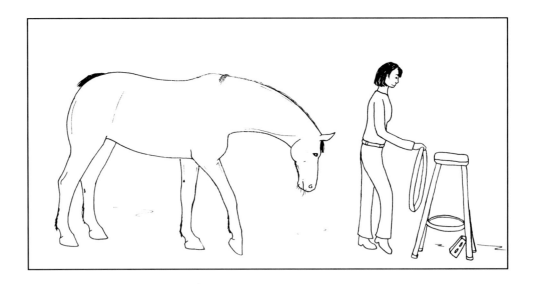

Sand tray activities can be a great experiential way to encourage conversation and visualize concepts that we struggle to articulate. By using a round pen and larger items, participants can create a sand tray large enough for a horse to interact with. Participants can later share how they felt observing the horse's interactions with their objects as well as ponder what the horse represented in their individual sand tray worlds.

This activity can be done in a divided round pen with participants with addiction or opposing worlds. Example: the left side of the round pen represents their past and the right their future. Build what their world looks like on each side and prepare to share with the group what was built.

"Carol explained her world to the group. The horse walked through her world and then pooped right next to it. The group laughed but Carol did not. She stated that was exactly how she felt. Walked over and crapped on while everyone just stood by and laughed."

OBJECTIVE

Create a large sand tray therapy opportunity using a variety of objects and a horse at liberty.

MATERIALS NEEDED: A variety of objects such as pool noodles, stuffed animals, road cones, pool toys, risers, ground poles, barrels, hula hoops, and balls.
HORSES NEEDED: Passive extrovert horse. (Refer to the Horse Interaction Index.)
SET UP: Open the room or area that has the objects in it. Prepare horses to bring into the activity once participants have started building their worlds. Professionals will need a large round pen or open arena depending on the size of the group. Preferably, professionals should create a tight intimate space if possible, allowing more of an opportunity for the horse to interact with the participant's worlds. This space can be indoors or outdoors, depending on the facility and barriers, like ground poles or temporary fencing that can be set up to create a tighter space.

INTRODUCTION

Sand tray therapy is an experiential activity in which participants can play in a large sand tray and discuss their emotions or struggles. Some examples of activities done using sand tray therapy in a traditional office setting are raking the sand, constructing something in the sand, and burying or finding objects in the sand. Sand tray therapy is an effective activity for participants who have suffered a traumatic event because the "tactile, nonverbal experience promotes awareness of deeply personal emotional issues within a safe, therapeutic environment"[10].

Ask participants to choose up to seven objects from the object closet or area that represent something significant in their lives. Examples could include: children, spouses, houses, pets, their rehabilitation, their job, etc. Next, ask the participants to go to the arena or round pen and construct their worlds using the significant objects they chose.

SIDELINES

Not giving participants an exact number of objects to choose from allows the freedom for participants to choose many objects or limit themselves and create a minimalistic world. Once the building has begun and the horse is introduced, the interaction with the horse in each participant's world and the participant's frustration or reaction to the horse's actions can be meaningful. If necessary, use a time restriction for this activity.

A good group size for this activity is six participants. Having more than this can lead to a processing session that is too long and drawn out for all participants to remain engaged. This activity can also be done with an individual participant who builds his or her world in an arena or a round pen and then processes the items chosen and the horse's interaction with his or her world.

The optimal setup for this activity should look like this:

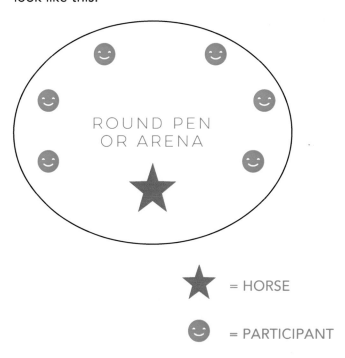

PROCESSING POINTS/ APPLICATION

- Everyone has a different world: what role did the horse play to your world (chaos, support, visitor, destructor)?
- Even though you built just your world, if you take a step back the other worlds are a part of your world as well.
- What would you change in your world if you could?
- What did you forget in your world?
- Who did you include or not include?
- Where are you in your world?

You may also explore the meaningfulness of colors, shapes, textures, and toys chosen.

THERAPEUTIC OUTCOME

The expected therapeutic outcome for this activity is that participants will be able to explain the reasons why they chose the objects to create their world as well as where the trauma and depression in their lives appears in their world. The participants should be able to realize in the processing segment that their world is surrounded by other group member's worlds. They should identify what the horse represents in their world and recovery. By seeing that their world is only a part of the round pen or the entire ranch and that they are not isolated or alone but part of a group, trauma survivors may think less about isolation and more about inclusion[11].

Interacting with a horse in a group equine-assisted psychotherapy session has increased the social skills of participants and given participants the confidence to interact with other members of the group[8]. In a traditional clinical rehabilitation setting there is an obvious lack of opportunity for equine interaction. Studies demonstrate playing with horses can lead to an increased rehabilitation from social isolation and lack of confidence present with participants suffering from trauma and depression[8].

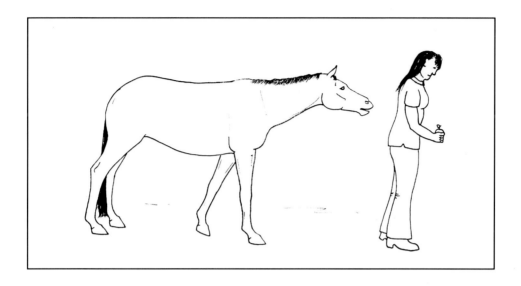

Often, we find that individuals have trouble establishing healthy boundaries. This can be a great topic of conversation. Without setting boundaries, and seeing how a lack of boundaries can be harmful, there can be lack of motivation to change. This activity provides visual examples of boundaries being pushed, walked through, and violated in a safe manner. ***Horse selection is very important for this activity.***

"A group from a large company's sales team came out to the ranch to work on some conflict resolution. One individual on the team historically never said no, resulting in overwhelm, frustration, and less than optimal results for performance. True to this individual's nature the horses mouthed, pushed, and nudged until they got what they wanted from the individual. From this interaction, not only was the team able to positively support the person who had boundary trouble, but he was able to see what happens when boundaries are set and that it can be about respect rather than letting anyone down."

OBJECTIVE

Set appropriate boundaries to keep horses from eating treats out of participants' hands and keep horses safe distance away from individuals and groups with treats using respectful boundary setting methods.

MATERIALS NEEDED: Carrots, ginger snaps, peppermints, apple snacks, or other horse treats, and a fenced area.

HORSES NEEDED: 1-2 extroverted and active horses to push the participants. (Refer to the Horse Interaction Index.)

SET UP: Give all participants 3 treats.

INTRODUCTION

Give participants treats and have them identify the areas of life that the treats represent where stronger boundaries are needed. Give the group instructions to not allow the horses to eat the treats and try to keep a minimum distance of 15 feet between horses and humans. Allow access into the open area and then put the horses at liberty in the open area as well.

SIDELINES

Identify which group members use avoidance as a source of setting boundaries. Observe interaction between group members and which group members choose to interact and try to feed horses despite instructions.

PROCESSING POINTS/ APPLICATION

- What does a healthy boundary look like?
- Should setting a boundary be negative and harsh, set in anger?
- Once a boundary is set do you ever have to re-set that boundary?
- Why are boundaries important?
- How do they keep us safe and successful in work and personal life?

THERAPEUTIC OUTCOME

The therapeutic outcome of this activity is that the importance of healthy boundaries are identified. Group members can identify what setting boundaries feels like and looks like. They may learn how to support other group members who struggle with setting appropriate boundaries. The group and individuals will be able to model and experience setting boundaries as well as to observe others who have more practice at maintaining their boundaries. Through processing, real life applications can be discussed inspired by interactions during equine activity.

Anyone who has participated or observed an equine-assisted activity has probably experienced a join up. It is one of the most commonly used and profound exercises in our toolbox of equine activities. This activity is no different than the common join up outcome. However, the approach and lead in looks a little different, resulting in what I believe is a more meaningful insight into the nature of energy and relationship.

The horse partners with an individual not because of control but because of trust, clarity of desire, and respect. The round pen is one of my favorite places on the ranch. There are no corners to a round pen, no place to hide. It represents a circle, a cycle, forward motion, a thing that is never ending, life, and so much more.

"**H**e struggled with sending the horse out to the rail. The horse returned to him time and time again as if to say, 'I know you do not want me to leave you'. He finally broke down in tears and hugged the horse. He whispered to the horse, 'I don't want you to leave me but if I do not take this time for me then I'll never be a good father and this cycle stops now. I do not want you to hate me like I hate my dad because I chose the bottle over my baby'. The round pen fell silent. As if a hidden cue was given, the horse trotted out to the rail and began circling the man. The horse kept his inside eye on the man, never glancing away. When the man stood tall, the horse began galloping. You could see the power, the energy, the joy of this forward motion. Movement is life to equines, and this horse felt more alive due to his human partner's energy. It was if the man and horse had both found permission to live. The man took a deep inhale, dropped his gaze and the horse slowed, stopped, turned, and walked into the center of the round pen. Right before the man and horse met, the man turned and walked shoulder to shoulder with the horse around the pen looking straight ahead with a purpose and a destination."

OBJECTIVE

Have the participant stand in the center of the round pen and the horse move around the rail at a walk, trot, or canter on cue with the energy of the human directing the horse. Using only energy and breath, cue the horse to run, walk, or approach the human and walk with the human around it.

MATERIALS NEEDED: Lunge whip, lunge line, and round pen.
HORSES NEEDED: Active introverted horse sensitive to energy. (Refer to the Horse Interaction Index.)
SET UP: Place lunge whip in center of area used.

INTRODUCTION

Tell the individual who will be remaining in the round pen to imagine a thin strand of twine tied from the their heart to the horse's heart. Keep the focus on that twine with their chest pointed towards the horse's shoulder. Have them decide which way they want the horse to move and use the hand that is closest to that direction to represent the future and the other hand to represent the past.

Remind the participant they are not going back to the past so they should keep their "past" hand behind the horse right at the horse's tail to encourage forward movement and close off the back. The other hand remains open, pointed not at the front of the horse but parallel with their body open to the future.

If needed, hold the lunge whip in the past hand to make a firmer energy to drive the horse into the future. Breathe and ask the horse to move into the future using only your hand signals and energy.

After this is successful, drop the lunge whip and take a deep breath. Avoid eye contact, drop your gaze, and imagine the horse walking towards you. If the horse remains still, approach it and gently squeeze the mane halfway down its neck. Turn and walk past the horse into the future and the horse should follow. Repeat the neck squeeze if not successful the first time focusing on intention and breath.

SIDELINES

Notice the energy, confidence, and body language of the individual who is in the center of the activity. Try whispering or speaking positive phrases and words to the individual as the activity is going and notice how this impacts the horse, human, and overall success of the activity.

PROCESSING POINTS/ APPLICATION

Positive statements, confidence and energy can all support the success of our future.

- How does breathing positively impact our clarity, confidence, and relationship?
- Is relationship about control or mutual respect and partnering?

THERAPEUTIC OUTCOME

The individual can recognize how meaningful their desires are by partnering and being found worthy of a relationship with a huge 1,200-pound animal.

This activity shows the power of intention and clarified focus. It is great for individuals who are working towards prioritizing their treatment goals or life goals.

Note: this is not a good activity for first time participants of equine activities. It requires a basic understanding of focused energy work and respect for the equine relationship.

"At only 13 she had learned that she should just keep her head down and that others' priorities were more important than hers. Or so she believed. She avoided eye contact with most people. As she held the end of the lead rope in her hands and pointed it towards the horse's hip, she saw his hip twinge. She took a breath, focused her gaze, and pointed again. This time he side-stepped. She smiled, gathered her thoughts and when she pointed the lead line again she found herself in a dance of respect and admiration with her horse. All she had to do was point or shift her body and he moved his in accommodation. It was the first time she ever felt important enough for someone to care about and like she had any impact on this world."

OBJECTIVE

Move the horse without touching it. Try side steps, turns, backing, and walking forward.

MATERIALS NEEDED: Lead line, halter, and open area.
HORSES NEEDED: Passive extrovert. (Refer to the Horse Interaction Index.)
SET UP: Use a confined space like a round pen or small pasture to contain energy and focus. Walk horse into area and unclip lead line from halter.

INTRODUCTION

Use the end of the lead line as a wand to direct the energy point at the horse's hip, trying to achieve a sidestep from the horse. Once achieved, try to have the horse continue to turn or side step until the "wand" is put down and the energy is released.

SIDELINES

Observe and later ask about body language, focus, and whether there is emotion with the energy or if it is simply focused intention. Ask the participant to note the equine's response.

PROCESSING POINTS/ APPLICATION

- What happens when we become frustrated with lack of results?
- Does it cloud our intentions or turn our calmer energy into harsh, frustrated energy?
- How can we use continued focus to obtain results?
- When are we most powerful — when we are focused on one thing or a dozen things?
- What is success?

THERAPEUTIC OUTCOME

Learn to clear one's mind and simply focus on one thing at a time. Learn to avoid becoming frustrated with lack of perception of success. Continue to pursue goals despite setbacks.

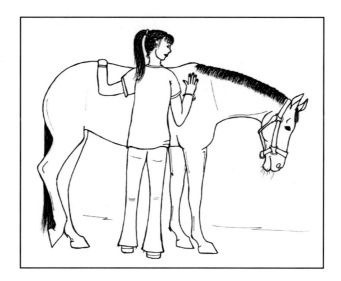

Mindfulness is an incredible activity to end the day with and culminate all the relationship work that has been done with the horse. The participants have an opportunity to spend some one on one time with the horse.

The stillness of this activity allows for all the mindful and impactful work of the day to really sink in. This activity is great for trauma populations who are learning self-care and insight into feeling, emotion, and relationships.

"**B**y matching her breath with the horse's, she was able to realize that she was actually holding her breath. When she heard the instructions to share a secret with her horse, she leaned in and told her horse something that she had never even openly admitted to herself. As she looked back into her horse's eye after sharing her secret she thought she saw her horse's gaze reflect compassion, understanding, and acceptance. Despite the horrible nature of her secret her horse continued to share space and love with her."

OBJECTIVE

Spend one on one time with a horse in a stall and engage in meditation through guided imagery and instructions on observations, breathing techniques, and physical contact with the horse.

MATERIALS NEEDED: Stalls and professionals to oversee interaction
HORSES NEEDED: Participant's choice. One horse for each participant.
SET UP: None needed.

INTRODUCTION

Allow participants to choose a horse to share stall time with. Give each participant access to the stall and leave door unlocked for safety. Tell them to choose the horse based on observation, not on the horse's name or story if they have one posted on the stall door. Once everyone is in a stall follow a script like this:

Using only your eyes begin to trace your horse's outline of their body. Begin at their forehead and gently trace over their ears, down their neck, over their back, hips, down their tail, across their hooves, up their legs and powerful thighs, under their barrels, down their tall front legs and up around their chest.

Circle your horse's jaw bone, trace down their face, over their nostrils, and up their face, finally returning to where you began. Now turn your attention to their eye. Pick whichever eye you can see best and look deep into it. What do you notice? What do you see reflecting at you? What does your horse see? What do you see?

Now slowly reach out and place one of your hands on your horse's shoulder. What is your horse's reaction? Begin to feel your horse's breath under your hand. Now imagine a white light that grows with each inhale from your horse. Imagine the white light pouring out from your horse and into your finger tips: warm, bright, positive, and comforting, growing larger with each inhale, and traveling further up your arm. Inhale it into your chest, your face, your stomach, down your legs, until you bring it all the way down your toes and you and your horse are sharing one surrounding light.

Now with each exhale feel any stress, overwhelm, concern, and negativity soften just a little bit. Imagine tiny bits of light coming through those feelings with each exhale until eventually you can saturate those feelings with that light, and all that is left is that white bright light that your horse has shared with you.

Now slowly slide your hand up over your horse's back over the midline and allow your body to drape over that of your horse's, chest to chest and heart to heart. Melt into your horse's body and lean into their support. Notice the power, the warmth, and the strength coming from your equine partner. Notice how they lean into you to make sure you do not fall. Bring your awareness to this feeling. Partnership, not equal but reciprocal, each being bringing their own energy and own unique aspect to this relationship. Begin to match your breath again with your horse's. Take 3 breaths here, even with your horse.

Now as you take your next inhale rise to a standing position again. Bring your awareness back to your horse's eye. What do you notice now? What has shifted or changed in what your horse sees reflected back to you? Has there been a shift?

When you are ready, think of something that you have not shared with anyone else. Think of a secret. Lean in and share your secret with your horse. Whisper words that no other person has heard, something you have been carrying around and can share with this strong supportive being in front of you.

When you are ready, in whatever time you

need, share gratitude with your partner and step out of the stall knowing that this is not goodbye but rather the beginning of a new path and journey that you are sharing with this new relationship.

PROCESSING POINTS/ APPLICATION

- What is it like to be fully supported: physically and mentally?
- How can you facilitate more of this in your life?
- What was it like to trust another being enough to confide in them knowing that you no longer have to keep that inside?

THERAPEUTIC OUTCOME

Builds trust, self-care, relaxation, and meditation.

ACTIVITY #10:
SADDLE UP

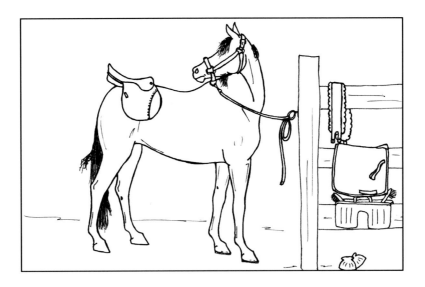

This is a more involved activity requiring a lot of oversight, a trusting horse, and more equipment. Remember that as the supporting professional, there is no wrong or right, there is just safe. If the saddle is on backwards, that is fine. It is all meaningful.

This activity can culminate in someone riding if that is appropriate and according to your safety standards for your facility. This activity is great for team building in corporate settings or building trust and identifying leadership techniques.

"He was positive that saddle pad was in the correct position. He listened to no one's input as he ordered around individuals. What resulted was that the saddle was too far back, the stirrups were not properly fastened, the cinch was backwards, and the horse was almost laughing at the lack of accuracy despite the arrogance of this individual. He would rather be unsafe than wrong and that was a clear theme in his professional life. Unwilling to accept help, guidance, feedback, or direction. It was costing him his job."

OBJECTIVE

Get the horse ready to ride.

MATERIALS NEEDED: Surcingle, saddle pad, riser, stirrups, reins, bridle, grooming box, extra pads, reins, helmet and odd items of tack that are not necessary for saddling this horse.
HORSES NEEDED: Passive introvert or extrovert that will not react to objects in the wrong place. (Refer to the Horse Interaction Index.)
SET UP: Place saddle and tack on fence of arena. Place grooming box on ground. Horse goes in arena on lead line with halter.

INTRODUCTION

Ask an individual or group to get the horse ready to ride. Gesture to items on the fence but provide no other specific instruction or direction.

SIDELINES

Ensure that equine remains calm and point out horse's reaction to the process. Make sure there is an equine professional present to supervise the activity. Remember that horse selection is vital in this activity.

PROCESSING POINTS/ APPLICATION

- Do you start with the task or the relationship and grooming?
- Could it be considered a success if you just got the horse clean and comfortable with the process and did not complete the saddle portion of the activity?
- How do you ensure that the horse's well-being is the center focus and how does that mean true success?

THERAPEUTIC OUTCOME

Treatment planning is understood from laying a foundation and preparing for higher goals in mental health. For corporate teams and therapeutic outcomes, communication and participant focus can be discussed.

OBJECTIVE

Create a scenario where not everything can be seen, but success is still an option. The tarp can represent sobriety, trust, relationships, a new chapter in life, or anything else that the professionals determine would be appropriate for the group. The objective is to have an experiential activity to illustrate that even though you do not have all the answers or knowledge at the moment, success is not impossible. Also, this scenario illustrates what we might take for granted or how our assumptions about things we do not know could impact our lives.

MATERIALS NEEDED: A large tarp. The use of paint or "obstacle" items is optional to hide under the tarp.

HORSES NEEDED: Passive Extrovert (Refer to the Horse Interaction Index.)

SET UP: Recommend using an outdoor arena for this activity to reduce echo noises from the tarp. However, if wind is a factor, please consider moving the activity to indoors. The idea is to create a scenario where the horse can safely cross the tarp while it is fully unfolded on the ground. I recommend introducing the tarp to the horse prior to the group or individual arriving at the ranch. Even if this is a horse that is familiar with the tarp, it is a good relationship builder to allow the horse to know what to expect and introduce the tool in a low stimulus environment. Unlock the room where you keep the objects or toys if you decide to use those for this activity. If you would like to use paint, be sure to have paint and water easily accessible.

EQUINE SAFETY NOTE: If you decide to hide obstacles under the tarp, participants will have to make a choice about how to get rid of or deal with these obstacles prior to putting the horse on the tarp. Please do not allow the horse to walk over the tarp while there are objects underneath the tarp.

INTRODUCTION

Bring participants out to the arena where the tarp is located. Present the tarp to the group folded up. Ask the participants what the object is and what it is used for. Most common answers include: protection, a barrier, to put something under, or to keep the rain off of something. Use their responses to state the objective of the activity. Explain that during this activity, the participants are going to be tasked with having the horse cross the tarp. Remember to remind the participants that the sound of a tarp can be intimidating for a horse because it sounds like wildfire which is extremely dangerous. Ask them how they think the horse is coping with the tarp. Listen to responses but do not discuss at length until after the activity. Most groups will initially fold the tarp up as small as possible to make this easy. Point out to the participants that although this makes the exercise simple, it is not realistic. Let the participants know that this was step one, and now we need to ensure that everything is being dealt with as realistically as possible. Would a horse deal with the tarp folded up or blown across the ground? Encourage the group to take small steps to assist the horse in learning that although the tarp is scary, it is manageable with support from other. Recommend they choose a safe way to handle their fears because avoiding it altogether is not an option.

BONUS

If you decided to use the obstacles in this part of the activity, then ask the participants to choose up to seven objects from the object closet or area that represent something they are ignoring or not dealing with in their lives. Examples could include: children, spouses, houses, pets, their rehabilitation, their job, etc. Then ask the participants to narrate how they are choosing to hide this obstacle or not deal with it as they hide it under the tarp. If you decided to use the paint, lay the tarp out and have participants describe what the paint (mess) represents that they are hiding. Then when the paint starts to mix with others, discuss how this impacts others and even though we think it might be pretty (i.e., working for us), what does it end up looking like?

SIDELINES

Observe how the participants choose to escalate the steps. How do they support the horse's reactions? Do they push or do they enable? Notice how emotional the participants become when the horse becomes scared. Does anyone give up or become disengaged? This activity can be a trigger for individuals who have PTSD due to watching another being become stressed.

PROCESSING POINTS/ APPLICATION

Some processing points could include:

- How do we neatly pack away our defenses?
- What is hiding under our own tarps?
- How much more dangerous did the tarp become when we hid our obstacles underneath it rather than deal with them?
- How long did it take for the horse to learn that no matter how big the tarp became, as long as the horse was in a trusting environment, it was still safe to manage?

THERAPEUTIC OUTCOME

The expected therapeutic outcome for this activity is that participants will be able to recognize that fear is not always debilitating. They can choose to take steps to manage and progress even when they are scared. It is far more dangerous to choose to ignore and not deal with their obstacles and set up barriers or defenses than it is to be supported and safely navigate them. Barriers can be protective but they should not be used to hide their defenses or obstacles.

ACTIVITY #12:
CODEPENDENT NO MORE

OBJECTIVE

Create an environment where two horses, normally pasture mates, can be separated in an arena and remain calm and comfortable even though they are apart from each other. Ideally one of the horses would remain with the group or individual while the other one is on the other side of the arena minding their own business.

MATERIALS NEEDED: A crop or lead line may be used to create a boundary but is not necessary.

HORSES NEEDED: If you have two horses that are pasture mates and become audible when separated, choose those two horses. The idea is that these horses normally stick together. The group or individual can make a new "herd" where the horses are comfortable not being with each other but instead stay a distance apart.

SET UP: Can be done in a pasture or arena. If done in a pasture, be aware of other horses around and how they might react. Put the horses at liberty to move freely.

INTRODUCTION

Discuss the definition of codependency with the group or individual. If you are in a professional learning environment, discuss how codependency can look in a professional setting. Discuss how an individual's identity can be dependent on their position or title. Ask the group to observe the two horses and choose the one with which they would like to partner. Their objective is to keep one horse with them at all times while keeping the other horse as far away from the horse they chose as possible while keeping both horses as calm as possible. Every time that a horse runs or becomes unsafe, the group must walk away from both horses and start again.

SIDELINES

Prior to giving the group the crop or lead line, observe what the participants do with the horses at liberty. Do they go right up to the horse's face, or do they allow some time for relationship building? If this is the second activity of the day, or the group has participated in activities before, then observe if the participants use their prior interactions with the horses to their advantage. Intervene anytime the professionals notice that the horse is becoming anxious as the goal is for the horse that the group chooses to prefer to be with the group than with the other horse. The other horse may occasionally need to be driven away from the group but in a non-aggressive manner. Observe if the entire group participates or if there is one leader.

PROCESSING POINTS/ APPLICATION

Discuss what setting healthy boundaries may look like in the participants' work life and home life (if appropriate).

- How did the group feel when they pushed the other horse away?
- How did the group feel when the horse did or did not join their group, and why does the group feel the horse made that choice?
- How long did it take to develop a trusting, safe relationship where the horse was not paying attention to the other horse?
- Why did the group choose that horse?
- What is a relationship in their lives that the individuals in the group can identify that may look like the one between these two horses?
- What steps can be taken to establish some safety and boundaries in that relationship?
- Did the boundary setting have to be mean or aggressive?

THERAPEUTIC OUTCOME

Participants realize that boundary setting is healthy and can be done in an effective manner without being mean or hurtful. Participants practice setting boundaries and setting up a healthy support network for their horse to be included and feel safe. Working as a group and a team is identified and practiced. Group and individuals practice remaining calm and de-escalating anxiety and fear when needed. Especially for military populations who move frequently, a way to become a part of a new community safely is practiced. This is also relevant and great for substance abuse populations who sometimes have to make new friends and set boundaries with family members who still drink or use.

OBJECTIVE

Practice focus and intention by mentally transposing a goal or dream to the concept of catching a horse. Use the power of intention, law of attraction, hard work, or whatever belief system the participant may want to engage in to catch the horse. Discuss how this is similar to the effort, energy, and mindset needed to create positive outcomes in our lives around goals and dreams.

MATERIALS NEEDED: Open pasture. Lead rope and halter if desired.
HORSES NEEDED: Typically a passive introverted horse; however, if you want to make the activity more difficult, choose an active introverted horse who will flee from an eager participant. To make the activity easier, choose an active extrovert who will willingly come to a participant who enters the pasture. (Refer to the Horse Interaction Index.)
SET UP: Leave a horse at liberty out in a field. There can be more than one horse in the field if necessary. Hang the lead rope and halter on the gate outside the pasture. Throw hay in the field if the horses will need it to remain happy during the activity.

INTRODUCTION

Instruct participants to imagine a dream or goal that they have. Encourage them to keep that dream or goal in their minds as they gaze out into the pasture. When they find a horse that they are drawn to, ask participants to imagine that their goal is that horse.

All they need to do is go catch it and it will be theirs. Remind them of the two requests brought up at the beginning of the day: 1. Remain present (for their safety and mindfulness), and 2. Trust. With these requests in mind, there should be less hesitation from participants to go into a pasture by themselves with a horse. Do not allow much clarification or questions with the goal that the participants do this activity in the way that seems most natural to them.

SIDELINES

Professionals will enter the pasture with the participants and wander with them, keeping an eye out for participants making unsafe choices such as running, walking behind a horse, etc. Observe each participant's interactions with their horse/goal. Do they blindly chase after it? Do they hold back in fear? Did they find and use the tools that were hanging on the outside of the pasture? Professionals may take a processing break in the pasture if frustration levels reach a therapeutic moment. This will allow for de-escalation and practicing of coping mechanisms. Notice how the participants communicate with their goals and themselves. This activity can lend to a verbalization of the negative or positive self-talk that participants often demonstrate in their lives.

PROCESSING POINTS/ APPLICATION

Some processing points could include:
- Be mindful of the self-talk used while pursuing goals.
- Notice what it took to achieve goals or dreams.
- What does your relationship with a dream or goal look like?
- Who do you have to support you as you pursue your dreams?
- What tools were needed in order to make the dream more attainable?

THERAPEUTIC OUTCOME

The expected therapeutic outcome for this activity is that participants will realize that dreams are there to be achieved. Simple steps can be taken today with the support and help of others to be closer to a dream or goal. It is dangerous to blindly run after a dream without regard of the consequences that it could have on other aspects of a life. The tangible outcome of catching a 1,200-pound animal when a participant has little to no equine experience can inspire trust, motivation, and commitment to dreams outside of the pasture, and reinvigorate what might have been a hopeless outlook.

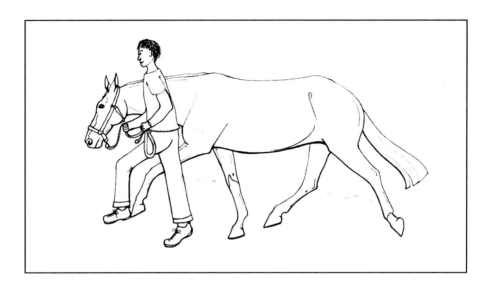

OBJECTIVE

Safely jog around an arena shouting a commitment or something the participant would like to be held accountable for while holding a lead line and leading an equine partner.

MATERIALS NEEDED: A lead line and a crop.
HORSES NEEDED: This horse selection is less about passive/active introvert or extrovert and more about which horse will be safest trotting next to participants unfamiliar with leading horses.
SET UP: An open arena sized so that a participant can jog around it in less than three minutes. An outdoor arena would be preferable as participants will be yelling throughout the activity.

INTRODUCTION

Ask participants to identify one thing for which they would like to be held accountable and for which they need help from the group in being held accountable. Have participants tell their chosen commitment or statement to either the professionals or the group, and allow the professionals or group to hold their thumbs up or down to indicate whether they agree and commit to holding the individual accountable for this statement or not.

If a participant does not receive unanimous thumbs up, then process and discuss with group why this occurred. When the participant has their approved commitment or statement, hand the participant the leadline and instruct them to jog slowly around the perimeter of the arena while shouting their accountability statement repeatedly for all of the rest of the group to hear. Instruct them to "whoa" their horse when they are 15 feet away from the last corner of the arena.

SIDELINES

Observe how the participant reacts to feedback from professionals or groups. Notice how the horse reacts when the participant takes hold of the horse, and how the partnership looks as the participant jogs around the arena. Make sure that a horse handler shadows the participant as they jog to encourage safety. When they ask the horse to "whoa," notice how quickly the horse stops. Then start the process over with another participant if this is a group activity. If this is an individual activity, professionals could choose multiple commitments to work on with the participant during this activity, or perform multiple rounds in the arena with one commitment with the participant.

PROCESSING POINTS/ APPLICATION

- Ask the participant how it felt to hear those words out loud.
- What did they feel when the group was providing them with feedback about their commitment?
- What was their perception about how committed the horse felt while the participant was jogging and the horse was listening to the statement?
- Process the connection between how easily the horse "whoas" to how dedicated the participant is to stopping their behavior or quitting whatever is necessary to achieve their commitment.

THERAPEUTIC OUTCOME

Participants are involved in this learning or therapeutic activity to make a change. No matter how small, they came to learn something about themselves so participants could then make decisions about future choices with that insight. This is an incredible high energy activity to bring life to that choice. If a participant has relapsed or tried to change in the past and struggled, then this activity is great for making the irst commitment and having a group to support that commitment through holding each other accountable. The voting portion of this activity ensures the participant does not focus on the wrong things in order to make meaningful change in their lives, and provides a chance for them to hear how their support network perceives their commitment or choices that they are making. Pairing the physical exertion with the verbal commitment brings a higher level of energy to the process versus just traditional talk therapy or accountability in a professional setting.

OBJECTIVE

Support a participant and horse through a mounted ride with safety and security being the primary focus for both the participant and horse. This is a trust exercise through and through. This is the only mounted activity in the entire manual and can be used as a ground activity as well.

MATERIALS NEEDED: Tack for the horse and also extra tack items that will not be used. Include a helmet and grooming supplies. Note: It is up to the professional if the helmet is brought out or if the helmet is the correct size. This can lead to a processing discussion around preparation and safety.

HORSES NEEDED: Passive extrovert horse. (Refer to the Horse Interaction Index.)

SET UP: An open arena where a horse can be held while being tacked and where multiple individuals can move around the horse safely and confidently without walking behind the horse. A horse handler will be needed to hold the horse.

INTRODUCTION

Ask participants which one of them needs to work on trust and balance the most out of the group. Allow them to discuss and choose one individual. Explain that their objective is to have the individual that they choose safely and securely ride this horse.

Do not say the participant will ride today. Just leave this open ended. Again, refrain from answering any questions or any further directives. The group has all of the tools needed. This activity is about observing how the group solves and works together on problems.

SIDELINES

Once given the objective and the tools, notice what the group prioritizes. Most groups will immediately begin tacking the horse rather than beginning with grooming. If necessary for safety, have a horse handler lead the horse.

PROCESSING POINTS/ APPLICATION

This activity is ripe with processing points. From the very beginning, the group can discuss why they chose the participant that they did and what they identified as the obstacles with balance and trust. Then as the activity progresses, professionals can question why the group started with the tools that they did, how grooming sets a strong foundation, and how this corresponds to self-care. Then the group can move into working as a team to identify which tools were needed to tack the horse and create a safe experience for the participant.

- Did the group even consider if the participant wanted to ride today?
- Was the participant included in the conversation?
- Did the group ask for help, and if so, did they expect it to be done for them?
- Did the group take time to build a relationship with the horse or did they just start tacking?
- Does the group know how to lead a horse safely, and was this discussed and practiced?
- How was the participant's anxiety or emotions discussed and handled?

- How was the participant made to feel supported?
- How was the horse made to feel supported?
- Was "good enough" safe for the participant?
- How is this like their lives when doing something halfway could be dangerous?
- How did the group handle the extra tools?
- What is extra in the participants' lives or roles that they do not need?

THERAPEUTIC OUTCOME

Depending on how the activity goes, there are a lot of therapeutic outcomes to this activity. It may take a while to fully process. Ultimately, the participant might not mount the horse at all, making this a ground activity, and it would still carry the majority of the processing points listed above. Often in life, participants start from the middle rather than the very beginning, which is a valuable lesson to receive from this activity. If the group does manage to make it to having the participant safely mount the horse, and a professional who is comfortable and certified to have a mounted rider during the activity is present, then the group can process what steps it took to get to that point, and the ongoing communication from the ground, the rider, and the horse in order to make it successful. A great outcome for this activity is that the group realizes that the first step to success is usually 15 steps before the one they assumed was first, and that self-care and care for others plays a huge part in that success.

OBJECTIVE

Participants create art inspired by herd observation. They discuss their perceptions of the herd and how this relates to their therapeutic or professional settings. This activity is intended to be a low intervention activity where an equine professional or horse handler is not needed; only a facilitator and if necessary a mental health professional are required.

MATERIALS NEEDED: Canvases, paper, or other medium, boards and easels on which to paint, paint or instruments to draw and create, brushes if necessary, and chairs.
HORSES NEEDED: A pasture with one or more horses.
SET UP: Set up chairs and easels outside of the pasture where clients can easily view horses.

INTRODUCTION

Present the pasture and art utensils to participants and instruct them to paint or draw what they see. Encourage them to take into account the story of the animals, their energy, and anything else they observe from the horses.

SIDELINES

There is little sideline work for this activity other than to walk around and see if participants need any additional tools for their painting or drawing. This starts as a group processing activity but becomes an individual activity during the actual creation process. Professionals should try not to impact the participant's impressions with conversation or observations.

PROCESSING POINTS/ APPLICATION

- How do participants explain their art?
- What did they see?
- What experiences in their lives impacted their paintings?
- Did they get a good idea of the horse's story from the herd observation?
- What did they see, and how is that reflected in their artwork?
- What colors or mediums did they choose?
- What will they do with their artwork now?
- How would their art be different in a few days, weeks, or years?

THERAPEUTIC OUTCOME

Again, this activity is purely a low impact, low intervention activity to allow participants a steady stream of outlet without necessarily having to interact physically with a horse. This should reduce fear and pressure and allow for a calm and enjoyable experience. There is no right or wrong to their creations. The reflection on their pieces is a time to build community and relationship with other group members as well as confidence in themselves.

ENDNOTES

1   Kohanov, Linda (2003). *Riding Between the Worlds*. Novato, CA: New World Library.

2   Van Der Kolk, B., (2014). The Body Keeps the Score: Brain, Mind, and Body in the Healing of Trauma. New York, NY: Penguin Group.

3   Matuszek, S. (2010). Animal-Facilitated Therapy in Various Patient Populations: systematic literature review. *Holistic Practice, 24* (4), 187-203.
     nursing

4   Foa, E., Hembree, E., & Rothbaum, B. O. (2007). *Prolonged Exposure Therapy for PTSD: Emotional Processing of Traumatic Experiences Therapist Guide*. Oxford University Press.

5   Frewen, P. A., Evans, E. M., Maraj, N., Dozois, D. J., & Partridge, K. (2008). Letting go: Mindfulness and Negative Automatic Thinking. *Cognitive Therapy and Research, 32*(6), 758-774.

6   Herman, J. L. (1997). *Trauma and recovery*. New York, NY: Basic books.

7   Kilpatrick, D. G., Ruggiero, K. J., Acierno, R., Saunders, B. E., Resnick, H. S., & Best, C. L. (2003). Violence and risk of PTSD, major depression, substance abuse/dependence, and comorbidity: results from the National Survey of Adolescents. *Journal of Consulting and Clinical Psychology, 71*(4), 692.

8   Maujean, A., Kendall, E., Lillan, R., Sharp, T., & Pringle, G. (2013). Connecting for health: Playing with Horses as a Therapeutic Tool. *Journal of Community Psychology, 41*(4), 515-522.

9   Lambert, M. J., & Barley, D. E. (2001). Research Summary on the Therapeutic Relationship and Psychotherapy Outcome. *Psychotherapy: Theory, Research, Practice, Training, 38*(4), 357.

10   Webber, J., & Mascari, J. B. (2008). Sand Tray Therapy and the Healing Process in Trauma and Grief Counseling. In *Based on a program presented at the ACA Annual*

11   Foy, D. W., Eriksson, C. B., & Trice, G. A. (2001). Introduction to Group Interventions for Trauma Survivors. *Group Dynamics: Theory, Research, and Practice, 5*(4), 246.

ABOUT THE AUTHOR

Bunny Young is an Army Wife who was diagnosed with a heart condition at a young age. Being dependent on a service dog has cultivated in Bunny an emphasis of inclusion and sensitivity for all populations. With a Master's Degree in Counseling and Psychology with a concentration in Equine Assisted Mental Health from Prescott College, Young has experience working with crisis response teams, first responders, trauma, depression, addiction, as well as criminal offenders.

She currently co-facilitates an equine program for inpatient addiction and has developed programs for use of equines to assist people with eating disorders, PTSD, counseling, cancer survivors, as well professional development programs for doctors, lawyers, and executives.

Young's consulting company, A Better Place Consulting, empowers and educates businesses and organizations about power of creating a positive work environment for employee and client retention.

She teaches leadership and cultural sensitivity to law enforcement and correctional officers, volunteers with Dreamcatcher's Therapeutic Riding, the Alzheimer's Association, March of Dimes and served as the Chair of the American Heart Association.

Young is also an active member of TRIAD, is on the Extraordinary Women's Exchange Committee, and is a Member of the Hanover Council on Aging. A national speaker, certified yoga instructor, and equine specialist who is competent in American Sign Language, Bunny Young is a powerhouse coach.

Bunny's favorite place to be in the world is riding with an equine partner. She enjoys the strong relationship she has with her Clydesdale she rescued, Paul, and riding with her two incredible daughters, Vyctoria and Rocky. She also is blessed with an incredible service dog named Guinness; a loving husband, Steve; and their other four-legged children, Titan and Kennedy.

ABETTERPLACECONSULTING.COM

Made in United States
North Haven, CT
20 December 2024

63341813R00027